MY POOP IS STUCK

Story by Khalil Dumas and Mary Parkinson

Art by Imani Dumas

Healthy Planet Press; Cape Coral, Florida, USA; healthyplanetpress.com

Library of Congress: 2019941943

ISBN: 978-1-7320462-5-2; First Edition

My poop is stuck.
It won't come out.

For breakfast, I ate
sausage, eggs with cheese,
and a carton of milk
I need to go, please.

I need to make
the brown, sewer snake,
a doodie, a dookie,
or a big, keister cake.

My dad says, "Bounce on the bed
To try and get it out.
Up and down, up and down,
Might bounce it out."

So I bounce on the bed.
I keep bouncing up and down.
I broke the bed, but the poop
will not come down.

For lunch, I ate
a cheeseburger and fries.
The poop is still stuck.
Oh why, oh why?

WELCOME
W
DRIVE THRU
W

I need to chop a log,
or drop a doo doo.
I need to make number 2,
or create a poo poo.

My mom says,
"Go read on the throne,
Try to work it out.
Take some time alone."

So I take a seat
and I start to read.
Twelve books already,
But I have no need.

For dinner, I ate
pizza with cheese.
I love to eat pizza,
But it doesn't love me.

My poop is still stuck.
My stomach really hurts.
I need to make some fudge,
or the chocolate squirts.

My sister says, "Come on,
Let's pedal our bikes around.
If we click-clack really fast,
The poop might come down.

We pedal down the hall;
Pedal around and around.
We click-clack, click-clack,
but the poop will not come down.

"Did you go yesterday?" Mom asks.
"No", I say.
"Well, enough is enough.
You need to poop every day."

"If I could do that on command,
I would be a poopologist or a
crapologist or a proctologist
(That's a butt doctor!)" I say.

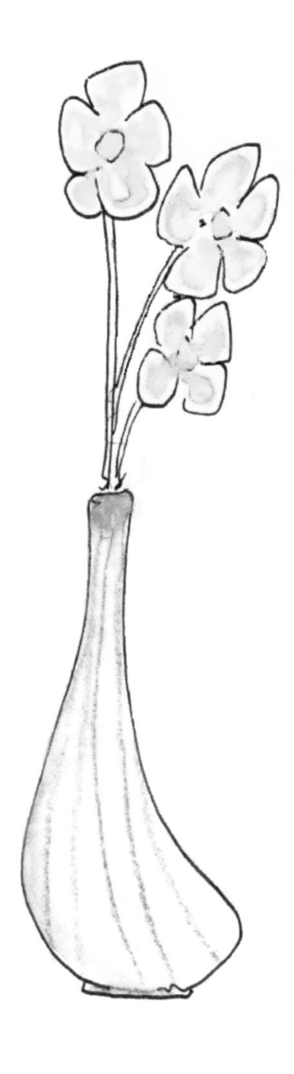

Mom says, "You are what you eat.
No more meats and cheese.
You need some fruits and
Vegetables, please."

So for breakfast, I ate
An apple, spinach, grapes
And a glass of water, too.
One hour later,
I might need to pooh.

My stomach starts
BUBBLING
TWIRLING
RUN

ling
Tumbling
Gurgling
Swirling
I need to go!

I jump off the bench,
And start running
Just as fast as I can
With poop to lose.

Hop over the cat,
Swing open the door,
Round the corner,
Slip on the floor.

HURRY, HURRY, HURRY,

Get out of my way
I will not poop
In my pants today!

Run in the bathroom,
Swing the door shut,
Throw down the seat,
Sit down and . . .

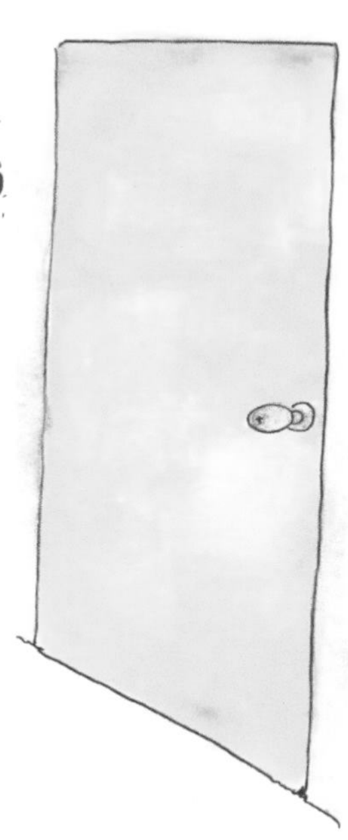

Plop,

Plop,

Plop,

AHHH

Relief !!

The True Story

My Poop Is Stuck is a true story about a boy, named Khalil. When Khalil was 3 years old, he did not poop for 21 days in a row. His poop was always getting stuck. The doctors wanted to remove his lower colon and reattach it (colectomy) because he was always constipated. Instead, we changed what Khalil ate, and he did not have surgery. Specifically, all dairy products were removed and meat was ate very rarely. Today, Khalil has a Bachelor of Science degree in Nutrition and Dietetics and is a healthy, vegan. Yes - that means no animal products (no meat, egg, milk, butter or cheese).

Khalil, a healthy vegan

Khalil, age 3

Look Before You Flush!

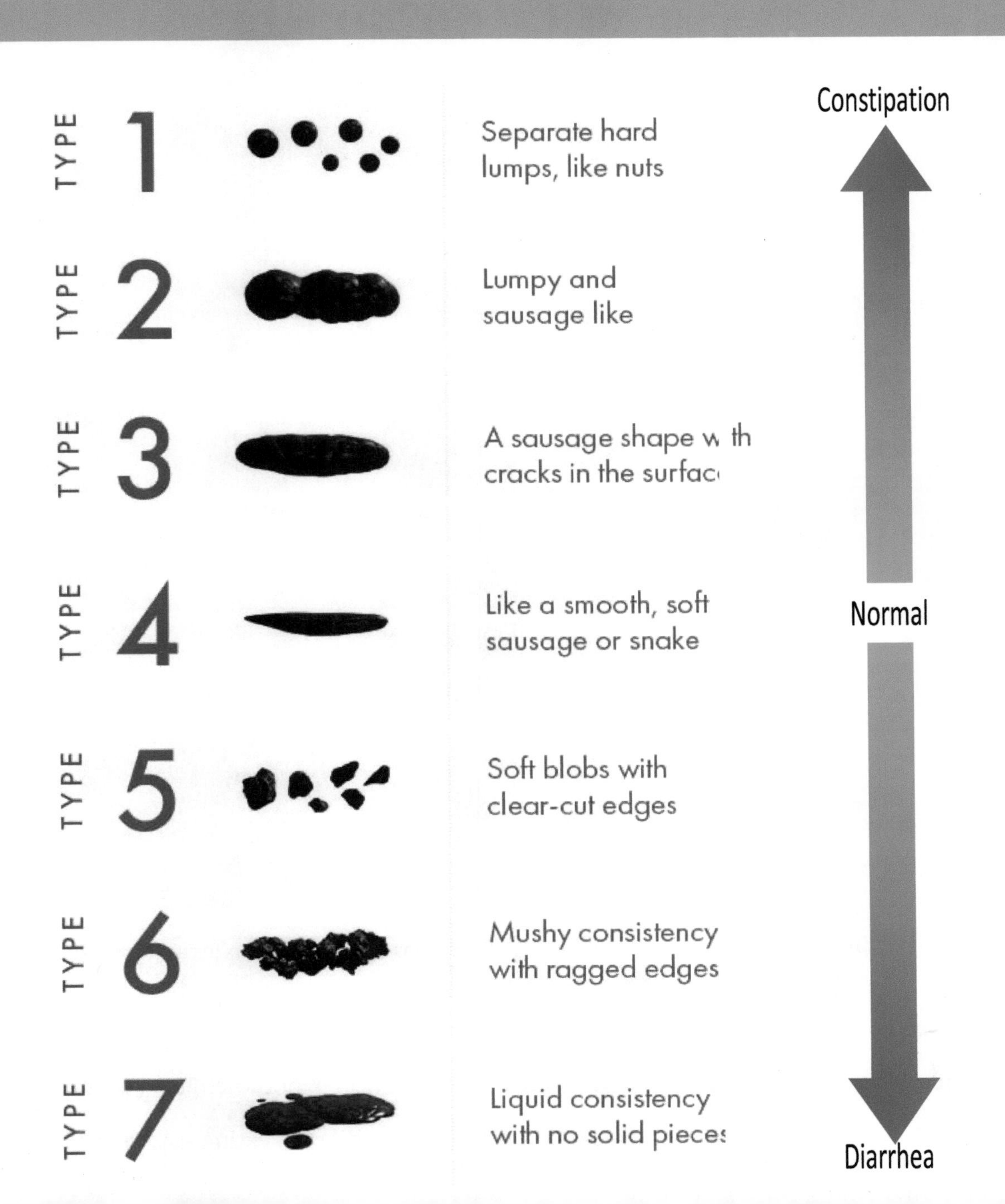

TYPE 1
Separate hard lumps, like nuts
TYPE 2
Lumpy and sausage like
TYPE 3
A sausage shape w th cracks in the surfac
TYPE 4
Like a smooth, soft sausage or snake
TYPE 5
Soft blobs with clear-cut edges
TYPE 6
Mushy consistency with ragged edges
TYPE 7
Liquid consistency with no solid pieces
Constipation
Normal
Diarrhea

CONSTIPATION

20% of pediatric visits are for constipation

16% of children suffer from chronic constipation

65 million Americans suffer from chronic constipation.

Normal Poop Range
4X/week to 3X/day

In studies, **elimination of all dairy products** cured almost all cases of childhood constipation.

Vegans poop the most and pass the softest stools. Eat plants!

Squat position helps. Put your feet on a stool and lean forward with your hands to the floor.

Foods That Help

Vegetables
Peas, Beans, Squash, Broccoli, Avocado, Kale, Carrots, Beets

Fruit
Raspberries, Prune, Plum, Apple, Mangoe, Figs, Pears, Watermelon, Grapes

100% Whole Grain
Brown Rice, Oatmeal, Whole Wheat, Barley

Beverages
Water, Hot Water with Lemon, Prune Juice, 100% Apple Cider, "Smooth Move" Tea

Crowley, Elesa T., et al. "Does milk cause constipation? A crossover dietary trial." Nutrients 5.1 (2013): 253-266.

Schmier, Jordana K., et al. "Cost savings of reduced constipation rates attributed to increased dietary fiber intakes: a analytic model." BMC Public Health 14.1 (2014): 374.

Sikirov, B. A. "Primary constipation: an underlying mechanism." Medical hypotheses 28.2 (1989): 71-73.

Davies, G. J., et al. "Bowel function measurements of individuals with different eating patterns." Gut 27.2 (1986): 16 169. Center for Disease Control and National Institute of Health Statistics

CPSIA information can be obtained
at www.ICGtesting.com
Printed in the USA
BVHW021451101220
595375BV00001B/2